Impressionist & Modern Art
1870-1970

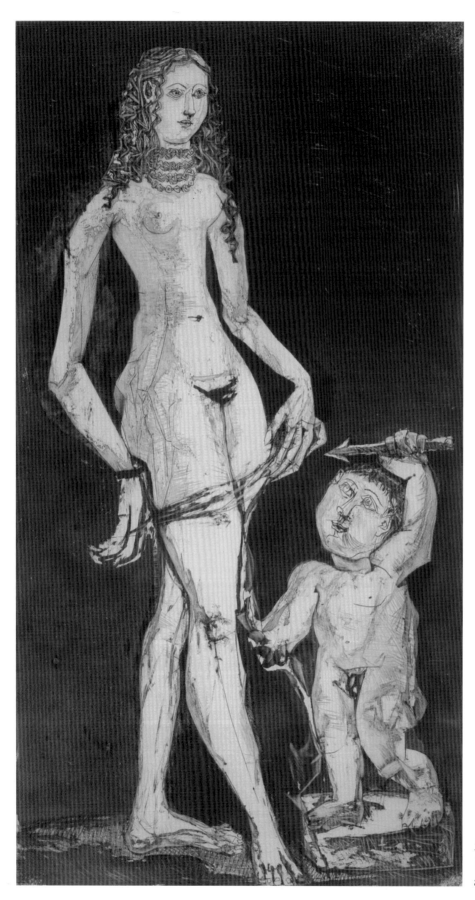

51. Picasso
Venus and Cupid
aquatint, 1949

Impressionist & Modern Art
1870-1970

*

Including Works By
Marcel Gromaire (nos. 34-46)
and
Pablo Picasso (nos. 47-61)

R. S. JOHNSON FINE ART
645 N. MICHIGAN, CHICAGO, IL 60611

(312)943-1661 FAX (312)943-1642

www.rsjohnsonfineart.com

Publication No. 150

*

*
Research
R. Stanley Johnson
Ursula M. Johnson
*

Special Assistance
Suzanne Varkalis
Liz Adamsick

On Cover:
20. Albert Gleizes (1881-1953)
Composition, 1920
Mixed media on canvas
35 x 28 3/4 inches
Signed and dated, lower right

26. De Chirico *Apollo and the Tulips*, mixed media

Index

1. **EDGAR DEGAS**
   Parisle 1834 - 1917 Paris

   Gentleman Rider, about 1870-73

   Pencil drawing
   410 x 260 mm.; 16 1/8 x 10 1/4 inches
   Cachet of *la vente de l'atelier Degas*, to lower right (Lugt 658).

   References:
   1. Paris, 2-4 July 1919, Galerie George Petit, *Quatrième vente Degas*, no. 245a, reproduced.
   2. *Succession Jean Cau*, Beaussant Lefèvre, Paris, Drouot, Dec. 16, 1993: no. 51 and reproduced on page 34.

   Provenances:
   1. Studio of the artist, 1917.
   2. Jean Cau, Paris, 1993.

   Notes:
   1. A study related to the *Horse Rider* in the center right of the painting *Avant la course*, about 1873, National Gallery of Art, Washington, D.C., Lemoisne 317 (see: page 160 of *Degas*, Grand Palais, Paris, 1988). The part of this drawing *Backs of Horses* relates also to Lemoisne 317 (see above) but appears even closer to the backs of horses seen in *Aux Courses en province*, about 1872, Museum of Fine Arts, Boston (Lemoisne 281). The rider of the horse in this drawing could be Paul Valpinçon, at whose country estate Degas had spent some time in the early 1870s.
   2. The late Jean Cau, the former owner of this drawing, was a well known French writer, journalist and collector. Over the decades, he usually could be found in one of the cafes on or just off the rue de Seine in Paris.

   Collection:
   A private collection

2. GUSTAVE DORÉ
Strasbourg 1832-1883 Paris

Le Songe d'une nuit d'été, circa 1870
A Midsummer Night's Dream

Watercolor
482 x 381 mm.; 18 15/16 x 15 inches
Cachet of the studio, lower right

Provenance:
Galerie Alfa, Paris

Notes:
1. In 1866, Doré moved to London where he became fascinated with British Romantic authors. In the following decade, Doré created illustrations for Milton's *Paradise Lost*, Tennyson's *Idylls of the King* as well as for other works by Lord Byron and Dickens. In *La Vie et l'oeuvre de Gustave Doré*, published in Paris in 1983 (p. 188), Doré is quoted as saying that his "intention is to make Shakespeare my masterpiece". This Shakespeare project, except for his illustrations for his *Macbeth* of 1870 and other individual studies, was never completed.
2. This particular watercolor by Doré appears to refer to the end of Scene I ("A wood near Athens") and/or Scene II ("Another part of the wood") both from Act II of Shakespeare's *A Midsummer Night's Dream.*

Act II, Scene 1(A wood near Athens), lines 249-254: Oberon.

> *I know a bank where the wild thyme blows,*
> *Where oxlips and the nodding violet grows,*
> *Quite overcanopied with luscious woodbine,*
> *With sweet musk roses, and with eglantine.*
> *There sleeps Titania sometime of the night,*
> *Lulled in these flowers with dances and delight…*

Act II, Scene 2 (Another part of the wood), lines 1-8

> *Enter Titania, Queen of Fairies, with her train*
> *Titania. Come, now a roundel and a fairy song;*
> *Some war with reremice for their leathern wings*
> *To make my small elves coats, and some keep back*
> *The clamorous owl, that nightly hoots and wonders*
> *At our quaint spirits. Sing me now asleep.*
> *Then to your offices, and let me rest.*

Collection:
A private collection

3. ODILON REDON
Bordeaux 1840 – 1916 Paris

Lumière (trial proof), 1893
Light

Lithograph
298 x 235 mm.; 11 3/4 x 9 1/4 inches
Annotated and signed by the artist: "lumière…Odilon Redon"

Reference:
André Mellerio *Odilon Redon*, published by the *Société pour l'Étude de la Gravure Française*, Paris, 1913: no. 123 and reproduced as plate no. 123.

Notes:
1. A rare and exceptional proof impression on *chine appliqué* paper. Before the edition of 50, which also was on *chine appliqué*, but with letters added below.
2. The date of this work marks a period of renewed interest in lithography. Kevin Sharp (in: *Odilon Redon, Prince of Dreams*, The Art Institute of Chicago, the Van Gogh Museum of Amsterdam and the Royal Academy of Arts in London, 1994-1995, pp. 240-242) notes:

> In 1890 Redon finally recognized that he could profit from eleven years of lithographic production by taking a more active role in the distribution of his new prints and in the marketing of his increasingly rare early lithographs. The relationship he had established with Destrée in Brussels …culminated in 1891 with Destrée's publication of a catalogue raisonné of the artist's lithographs…Redon tried to insure that the mounting enthusiasm for his lithographs would continue…he [even] removed the paintings and charcoal drawings he had left on consignment not only with [the dealers] Boussod and Valadon but also with Durand-Ruel, replacing them with lithographs…The change in Redon's fortunes reflected the growing interest in lithography…In April [of that year] the first major exhibition devoted to the medium opened at the École des Beaux-Arts in Paris…In July the critic André Mellerio [author of *Odilon Redon, Catalogue Raisonné* of the artist's lithographs in 1913] proclaimed that the renaissance of lithography was occurring and he credited … [Redon] with single-handedly initiating it…

4. CAMILLE PISSARRO
St. Thomas, Antilles 1830-1903 Paris

Les Travailleurs aux Champs, about 1890-95
Workers in the Fields

Watercolor and pencil
286 x 219 mm.; 11 1/4 x 8 5/8 inches
Signed

Provenance:
1. Émile Strauss, Paris (sold: *Collection Émile Strauss*, Paris, June 3-4, 1929, no. 21)
2. Sale: Paris, June 10, 1937, no. 7
3. Sale: Paris, May 12, 1939, no. 33
4. P. Ebstein, Paris

Literature:
Ludovic Rodo Pissarro and Lionello Venturi, *Camille Pissarro, Son Art-Son Oeuvre*, vol 1, Paris, 1939, no. 1486, p. 286; vol. 2, no. 1486, illustrated p. 287

Notes:
1. There are two other works dating from this period in which Pissarro depicts the same female figure: a pastel in the British Museum and an oil entitled *Fenaison à Eragny* (see: Venturi no. 1207), in the collection of the National Gallery of Canada, Ottawa.
2. In this work, Pissarro refers to one of his favorite subjects: farm workers in the fields. This subject reflects the artist's special interest in the works executed at an earlier date by Jean-François Millet (1814-1875), an artist born sixteen years before Pissarro. This general subject was treated by Pissarro in many prints, drawings and paintings. In all of these media, the artist demonstrated a particular sensitivity to the light playing on each scene.

Collection:
A Private Collection

13

5. JAMES ENSOR
Ostende 1860-1949 Ostende

Hop-Frog's Revenge, 1898

Etching on copper plate
350 x 242 mm.; 14 1/8 x 9 7/8 inches
Signed lower right

Reference:
Delteil 112-II/II
Croquez 111-II/II
Taevernier 112-II/II

Formerly Collections:
Samuel Courtauld (with collector's mark). See: Douglas Cooper *Courtald Collection* catalogs no. 219.
A private collection, Chicago

Notes:
1. A superb, well-contrasted and early impression of one of Ensor's greatest graphic works.
2. Delteil, Croquez and Taevernier all list two states of this work. In the 2nd State the charred body of one of the victims is shown fallen on the ground. Taevernier notes still other numerous changes distinguishing the second from the first state.
3. According to Croquez, this etching was inspired by a tale of Hans-Christian Andersen. Taevernier, on the other hand, believes (correctly) that the scene derives from a short story, *The Hop-Frog*, by Edgar Allan Poe and he sums it up as follows:

> The dwarf Hop-Frog is the king's jester and takes his revenge on the king and his ministers for their wrongs done to his companion, Trippetta. The dwarf organizes a masked ball which the king and his seven ministers are to attend as a group of men, tarred and chained together. They present themselves to the masked spectators crowding the balconies of the king's immense banqueting-hall. The dwarf, having first removed the great chandelier, manages to hook the group of men with the chain of the chandelier and lift them high in the air. He himself then climbs [above the king and his ministers] and with a flaming torch in his hand sets fire to the tarred men crying "I see a great king and his seven privy-councilors, a king who does not scruple to strike a defenseless girl...As for myself, I am simply Hop-Frog the jester and this is my last jest." Hop-Frog then clambers to the ceiling and escapes with Trippetta onto the roof.

After having gotten rid of the king and ministers, following Edgar Allan Poe's text, Hop-Frog, the jester, and his companion, Trippetta, left the country to pursue their happiness together. They were never to be seen again.

6. MARY CASSATT
Allegheny, near Pittsburgh 1844 - 1926 Mesnil-Théribus, Oise

By the Pond, about 1896

Dry point and color aquatint
330 x 429 mm.: 13 x 16 7/8 inches
Signed, lower right

Reference:
Breeskin 161
Mathews/Shapiro 21-IV/IV

Notes:
1. A very fine impression, with pristine colors, of this major and now very rare color aquatint by Mary Cassatt.
2. In this work, each of the plates for each color of each impression was inked and printed separately, all of which took a great deal of skill, time and effort. The total edition of this work probably would not have exceeded fifty. From the impressions printed, according to Mathews/Shapiro (*Mary Cassatt: The Color Prints*, Nancy Mowll Mathews and Barbara Stern Shapiro, Williams College Museum of Art, 1989), as of 1989 seventeen are known to be in the following public institutions:

> Art Institute of Chicago
> Bibliothèque d'Art et d'Archéologie (Fondation Doucet), Paris
> Baltimore Museum of Art, inscribed to George Aloysius Lucas(1824-1909)
> Bibliothèque Nationale, Cabinet des Estampes, Paris
> The Brooklyn Museum
> Carnegie Museum of Art, Pittsburgh
> Cleveland Museum of Art
> Honolulu Academy of Arts
> Library of Congress, Washington, D.C.
> The Minneapolis Institute of Arts
> Museum of Modern Art, New York
> New York Public Library, inscribed to Samuel Putnam Avery (1822-1904)
> Oregon Art Institute, Portland Art Museum
> Philadelphia Museum of Art
> St. John's Museum of Art, Wilmington, North Carolina
> Smith College Museum of Art, Northampton, Massachusetts
> Terra Museum of American Art, Chicago and Giverny

7. JEAN-BAPTISTE-ARMAND GUILLAUMIN
Paris 1841 – 1927 Paris

Bords de Creuse, about 1895
Banks of the Creuse River

Oil on canvas
629 x 914 mm.; 24 7/8 x 36 inches
Signed, lower right

Provenance:
R. S. Johnson Fine Art
Private Collection, Philadelphia

Exhibited:
Guillaumin, Serret-Fauveau Collection, Paris, 1954: no. 10

Notes:
1. An exceptionally fine and beautiful painting by Guillaumin. *The Bords de la Creuse* (Banks of the Creuse River) is one of the artist's most sought after subjects.
2. Together with Monet, Renoir, Pissarro and Degas, Guillaumin participated in seven of the eight Impressionist exhibitions which took place between 1874 and 1886. In both his pastels and paintings, Guillaumin was constantly in advance of his times. His works, such as this one from circa 1895, place him as a precursor of the Fauve movement, which took place some ten years later in 1904-1907.
3. This work will be included in the *Guillaumin: Catalogue Raisonné* being prepared by Dominique Fabiani and Philippe Cazeau.

8. JEAN-BAPTISTE-ARMAND GUILLAUMIN
Paris 1841-1927 Paris

Le Puy Barriou, about 1903

Oil on canvas
630 x 930 mm.; 24 ¾ x 36 5/8 inches
Signed lower right

Notes:

1. The importance given to Guillaumin by Dr. Paul Gachet (Van Gogh's doctor) and by Gachet's son, Paul Gachet, was shared through the esteem of Cézanne and Van Gogh. In a letter written to the painter Emile Bernard (*Lettres de Vincent Van Gogh à Emile Bernard*, 1911, p. 75, letter 1; and also quoted in the recent exhibit: *Dr. Gachet: A Friend of Cézanne and Van Gogh*, New York, Paris and Amsterdam, 1999-2000 exhibit p. 144), Van Gogh writes:

   > I believe that, as a man, Guillaumin possesses better thought-out ideas
   > than the others and that if all [of us] were like he, much better art would
   > be being produced...

   It in fact was to bring attention to "the least understood of the impressionists" (see: *Dr. Gachet*, ref., above, p. 144) that, in his gift to the Musée d'Orsay in Paris in 1949, the son of Dr. Paul Gachet, at the same time that he gave Van Gogh's *Self-Portrait and Portrait of Dr. Paul Gachet*, also gave Guillaumin's *Self-Portrait* of 1870-1875.

2. This fine work, one of the artist's rare winter landscapes and with extraordinary color harmonies, will be included in the *Guillaumin: Catalogue Raisonné* being prepared by Dominique Fabiani and Phillippe Cazeau.

9. ALBERT LEBOURG
Montford sur Risle 1849 - 1928 Rouen

Paysage au bord de l'eau
River-Bank Landscape

Wash drawing
230 x 300 mm.; 9 x 11 3/4 inches
Signed, lower left

Notes:
1. This fine Lebourg wash drawing appears to depict a scene on the Seine River near Rouen. This was the region in which Lebourg spent almost his entire creative life.
2. Together with Degas, Monet and Pissarro, Lebourg participated in the 4th Impressionist exhibition of 1879 where he showed ten paintings and nine drawings. Exhibiting twenty paintings and ten drawings, Lebourg also took part in the 5th Impressionist exhibition of 1880. This latter exhibition included Mary Cassatt, Degas, Guillaumin, Morisot and Pissarro.

10. ALBERT LEBOURG
Montford sur Risle 1849 - 1928 Rouen

Les Bords de la Seine à Caumont en eté, 1911
The Banks of the Seine River at Caumont in the Summer

Oil on canvas
460 x 760 mm.; 18 1/8 x 29 7/8 inches
Signed, located and dated, lower left: *Lebourg Caumont 1911*

Notes:
1. Lebourg's roots were in Normandy and particularly Rouen where his painting had been appreciated since the early 1870s. His recognition in the Parisian world came with his participation in 1879 in what now is designated as the 4th Impressionist Exhibition. This exhibition, which took place at 28 avenue de l'Opéra in Paris, included Caillebotte, Cassatt, Degas, Monet, Pissarro as well as Lebourg who showed twenty paintings and ten drawings. Subsequently, Lebourg took part in the 5th Impressionist exhibition in Paris in 1880. The artists in this latter exhibition included Caillebotte, Cassatt, Degas, Guillaumin, Lebourg, Morisot, and Pissarro. In the 5th Impressionist exhibition, Lebourg presented ten paintings and sixteen drawings and watercolors.

2. Recognition of the importance of the Impressionists by French museums gained considerable momentum through the gift (which included 13 paintings by Lebourg) of the collector François Depeaux to the Musée des Beaux-Arts in Rouen in 1909. At the time of this gift, Depeaux stated (quoted in: François Lespinasse, *Albert Lebourg*, Rouen, 1983: p. 206):

   > ...this collection seems to me to give a good idea of what has been called Impressionism, but what could be more correctly called the School of Open-Air Painting (*école en plein air*). [Our purpose is] to open widely the doors of this museum to an art which, although very criticized at its beginnings and even up to just a few years ago, finally through the truth and ardent conviction of its apostles, [that is to say] Cl. Monet, Sisley, Renoir, Degas, Cézanne, Pissarro, Guillaumin, Lebourg and all the following young [artists], now see their works classified among mankind's most beautiful [artistic] achievements...

3. To be included in the forthcoming *Lebourg: Catalogue Raisonné* being prepared by Rodolphe Walter, Wildenstein Institute.

11. MAXIME MAUFRA
Nantes 1861 - 1918 Poncé

Matin sur la rivière, Port Scorf, Morbihan, 1916
Morning on the River, Port Scorf, Morbihan

Oil on canvas
600 x 730 mm.; 23 1/2 x 28 3/4 inches
Signed and dated, lower right: *Maufra 1916*

Provenance:
Galerie Durand-Ruel, 1916 (inventory no. D20087, ex. 10943, Durand-Ruel photo no. 8298)
Private French collection

Reference:
Arsène Alexandre, *Maxime Maufra*, Galerie Georges Petit, Paris, 1926: p. 203 (where catalogued as one of the works executed by Maufra in *Bretagne* in 1916).

Notes:
1. In this painting, Maufra uses pictoral elements which he particularly loved: the coasts and the waterways of *Bretagne* (Brittany).
2. In the 1890s, Maufra was one of the artists of Galerie Durand-Ruel, the major dealer for the Impressionists. Durand-Ruel's artists included Cassatt, Degas, Guillaumin, Lebourg, Maufra, Monet, Moret, Pissarro, Renoir and Sisley. Maufra's representation was taken over at a later date by Durand-Ruel's leading competitor, Georges Petit, whose better-financed gallery also had obtained Sisley's contract already in 1888 and eventually was to handle other Impressionist artists including Monet. In 1926, Galerie Georges Petit published Arsène Alexandre's book, *Maxime Maufra*.
3. In: *Maxime Maufra*, Petite Encyclopédie des Peintres de Bretagne, Musée de Pont-Aven, 1998, page 30, the artist is quoted:

> My personal tendencies are to unite style and nature; to generalize landscape for a composition and, putting aside instantaneous impressions in order to express a more concrete sensation of these impressions ...As a Landscape-painter, I have painted everything that moves me, searching within nature, attempting to render the character of that which attracts me and to express in my work the emotion which I feel: Beautiful effects, which are clear or joyous; the torments of the elements; the calmness of solitude, the violence of storms and tempests.

12. JACQUES VILLON
Damville (Normandy)1875 – 1963 Puteaux

Comédie de Société, 1903
Comedy of Society

Etching and color aquatint with watercolor added
500 x 420 mm; 20 x 16 5/8 inches
Signed and dated, lower right

Provenance:
Francey and Martin Gecht, Chicago

References:
Auberty and Perussaux 43
Ginestet and Pouillon E.75

Notes:
1. Villon's dealer, Sagot, in 1903 described this work:

    > ....In a sumptuous interior, a hall decorated with green plants, three
    > ladies are sitting: two are together on a beige armchair, the other sits in a
    > blue and red armchair. The later is in an attractive pose, looking to the left
    > at a group of actors who are not visible from the left. The three women are
    > seen against a background of tapestry depicting various figures. The floor
    > is covered with a red rug.

2. This is perhaps the most complex and spectacular of all of Villon's color aquatints and apparently
    required seven different color-plates. The tapestry effect in the background is quite extraordinary.
    The light-blue in the hat of the central figure appears to have been added by the artist in watercolor
    in each individual impression. The hues of those "blues" vary considerably from one impression to
    another. The numbering indicates an edition of 50. However, each impression is different, depending
    on the varied inking of each of the color-plates. According to Ginestet & Pouillon, the model for
    each of these three women was Yvonne Duchamp-Villon, the wife of Villon's sculptor-brother
    Raymond Duchamp-Villon.

13. JACQUES VILLON
Damville (Normandy) 1875 – 1963 Puteaux

La Gouvernante, 1907-1909
The Nanny

Charcoal drawing with gouache on a partially lithographed background
470 x 350 mm.; 18 1/2 x 13 3/4 inches

Reference:
Ginestet & Pouillon *Jacques Villon: Les Estampes et les illustrations: Catalogue Raisonné*, Arts et Metiers, Paris, 1979: ref. *Illustrations de Journaux: Comœdia*, Dec. 11, 1909: no. 304, p. 489 (reproduction of illustration in *Comœdia*).

Notes:
1. A unique, trial study for a future illustration. With many lines executed in charcoal (for example, the background figures to the left) or gouache (for example, additions to the lady's hat) over a partially printed background. These added lines, in similar forms, eventually appeared as part of an illustration in the journal *Comœdia*. Below is Villon's hand-written text for this work.
2. This sensitively executed work depicts a Nanny (*La Gouvernante*) with two children, a boy and a girl, at the entrance of a puppet show. The scene most probably takes place in Paris in the Luxembourg Gardens where children, as seen in this work, are also offered pony rides.
3. This work in its final form, with printed text below and also with printed title above, was produced as an illustration which appeared in the journal *Comœdia* in Paris on December 11, 1909. The illustration was accompanied with a printed text which repeats the hand-written text of Villon seen in this preliminary study:

> *La gouvernante:*
> *"Et vous, Monsieur Paul, voulez-vous aussi entrer voir Guignol?"*
> *Monsieur Paul:*
> *"Oh, tu sais, moi, ma chère, je n'aime pas le théâtre."*

> The Nanny [speaking to one of the two children]:
> "And you, Monsieur Paul, would you like to go to see the puppet show?"
> Monsieur Paul [the little boy]:
> "Oh, you know, I, my dear, I do not care for the theater."

Comœdia

La Gourmante — Et vous monsieur Paul, vous ... aussi ... entre ... Guignol
monsieur Paul — ... tu sais moi, ma chère, Je n'aime pas le théâtre ...

14. JACQUES VILLON
Damville (Normandy) 1875 – 1963 Puteaux

L'Équilibriste, 1913
High-Wire Balancer

Oil on canvas
810 x 600 mm.; 31 1/2 x 23 1/2 inches
Signed

Exhibited:
Duchamp-Villon, Gleizes, Metzinger and Villon, Sturm Gallery, Berlin, 1914.
Cubism & La Section d'Or, Phillips Collection, Washington, D. C.; Dallas Museum of Art; and
the Minneapolis Institute of Arts, 1991: fig. 7 and repr. in color, p.144.

Literature:
Dora Vallier *Jacques Villon : Oeuvres de 1897 à 1956*, Cahiers d'Art, Paris, 1957: repr. p. 46.
Innis Howe Shoemaker *Jacques Villon and His Cubist Prints*, Philadelphia Museum of Art, 2001:
fig. 12, p. 39.

Notes:
The painting corresponds to Villon's 1913 drypoint *L'Équilibriste* (Ginestet & Pouillon E.286,
see illustration below), the most abstract of Villon's series of drypoints from 1913. Villon's
drypoint and this painting are both constructed, using the "perfect" triangles, quadrangles and
pyramids , based on the principles of *La Section d'or* (The Golden Section).

Collection:
A private collection

Villon   drypoint, 1913

15. JACQUES VILLON
Damville (Normandy) 1875 - 1963 Puteaux

Portrait d'Acteur (Félix Barré), 1913
Portrait of an Actor (Félix Barré)

Drypoint
400 x 315 mm.; 15 3/4 x 12 3/8 inches
Signed, dated 1913 and numbered 3/32

Provenance:
Collection of Jacqueline and Bernard Gheerbrant, founders of the *Librairie La Hune* at St. Germain-des-Près in Paris.

Reference:
Auberty & Pérussaux no. 199
Ginestet & Pouillon E. 283

Notes:
1. A superb impression of this work which many regard as Villon's *tour de force* among the artist's Golden Section period drypoints. Shoemaker (Innes Shoemaker, *Jacques Villon and His Cubist Prints*, Philadelphia Museum of Art, 2001: p. 28) refers to the dramatic effect of the drypoint in this work "as a result of the more aggressive crossing of planes, the stark contrasts of black and white, and the energetic linear hatchings that build the construction of planes...Villon allowed the compositional structure of planes and volumes to dominate the naturalistic representation of the subject, producing a work that is far more powerful than his Cubist drypoints to date". There is a pencil study for this work (private US collection : see illustration below).
2. The "actor" here is Félix Barré, a neighbor of Villon on the rue Lemaître in Puteaux. The Barrés and the Villons vacationed together on the Normandy coast. Villon had previously depicted Barré and his wife, nicknamed *La Bousine*, together with Villon's wife *Gaby* in a color aquatint of 1904: *Sous la tente, sur la plage (Blonville)*, (Ginestet & Pouillon E. 137).

Villon   pencil drawing, 1913

34

16. JACQUES VILLON
Damville (Normandy) 1875 - 1963 Puteaux

La Cage de l'Oiseau, 1955
Bird Cage

Oil on canvas
460 x 550 mm.; 18 1/8 x 21 5/8 inches
Signed and dated "55" lower right
Titled: *La Cage de l'Oiseau*, signed and dated "55" on verso

Provenance:
Galerie Louis Carré, Paris
Ragnar Moltzau, Oslo
Marlborough Gallery, New York (no. 1842)
Private European collection

Exhibited:
Kunsthaus Zürich, *Sammlung Ragnar Moltzau*, 1957
Dienst voor Schone Kunsten: Collectie Ragnar Moltzau,'s-Gravenhage, April-June, 1957: no. 118.

Literature:
Jacques Villon, Fogg Art Museum, Harvard University, Cambridge, 1976: repr. as plate 156c, p. 181.

Notes:
Villon first treated the subject of a bird in his etching *L'Oiseau* of 1921 (ref. Ginestet & Pouillon E. 293: see illustration below), then again in his 1932 etching *Nature morte au perroquet* (ref. Ginestet & Pouillon E. 362), and finally in his painting *L'Oiseau empaillé* of 1938. In the 1950s, he altered this subject, adding a cage and then wire bars. In 1952, Villon painted *La Cage et l'Oiseau* (private collection, Paris) in which the feathers are represented as simple, geometric shapes, separated by horizontal and parallel lines, signifying the cage. In this present painting, as pointed out in the above-cited Fogg catalogue, (text in this case by David S. Rubin, p. 180): "...the wires are seen from above, and the space is not illusionistic although the linear pattern deliberately alludes to a spider web as a metaphor for the cage". [In this as well as in other treatments of *La Cage et l'Oiseau*, Villon] "has delighted in contrasting forms and surface textures: the lines of the cage are played off against the dabbing and dotting of paint across the entire picture surface."

Villon   *L'Oiseau*, etching, 1921

17. FERNAND LÉGER
Argentan 1881-1955 Gif-sur-Yvette

L'Usine, 1918
Factory

Gouache
230 x 310 mm.; 9 1/8 x 11 3/8 inches
Initialed and dated, lower right

Provenance:
Galerie Louise Leiris (D.H. Kahnweiler), Paris

Exhibited:
Cubism & La Section d'Or, The Phillips Collection, Washington, D.C., March 9 - April, 28, Dallas Museum of Art, July 1-28, The Minneapolis Institute of Arts, October 5 -November 17, 1991: no. 23 and repr. p. 75.

Notes:
Fernand Léger, as seen in this scene and other early works, raises questions as to how his art relates or does not relate to that of Picasso.In his book *Der Weg zum Kubismus* of 1920 (pp. 40-41), Daniel Kahnweiler, the dealer for both Léger and Picasso, described "cubism":

> In accordance with its special role as both constructive and
> representational art, Cubism brings the forms of the physical world
> as close as possible to their underlying forms [*Urformen*]. Making
> use of these basic forms, upon which all visual and tactile perception
> is based, Cubism provides the clearest presentation and foundation for
> all forms...

In spite of their close relationship, Kahnweiler's concept of Cubism is very different from Picasso's. Whereas Kahnweiler begins his analysis from the abstract concept of the "skeletal frame", Picasso begins his paintings by focusing on the object itself. Kahnweiler's "skeletal frame" corresponds rather to the "perfect" triangles, pyramids and rectangles of the *Section d'or* (Golden Section) which were so important in much of the art of Juan Gris, Gleizes, Metzinger and Villon in particular and, to a certain extent, in the art of Fernand Léger. The questions are: what is "true" cubism and who are the "true" cubists? For Cooper and Tinterow, for example (see: Douglas Cooper and Gary Tinterow, *The Essentiasl Cubism: 1907-1920*, The Tate Gallery, London, 1983), only four artists were "true cubists", namely Picasso, Braque, Léger and Gris. This is a very discussible grouping. R. Stanley Johnson (*Cubism & La Section d'Or: Reflections on the Development of the Cubist Epoch 1907-1922*, 1991: p. 20) in analysing the idea of placing Léger among the "true cubists" wrote:

> The choice of Léger as one of the "true" Cubists is rather strange. In the
> years 1909-1912, he did employ certain pictorial elements in common
> with Picasso and Braque. Very differently from these artists, however,
> Léger respected the closed contours of the objects he depicted and, in his
> paintings, made use of visual effects taken directly from nature. In 1913,

(text continues on page 40)

by moving into total abstraction, Léger broke off completely with the basic principles of Picasso and Braque. In the following years, Léger's interests turned to the life of the modern city. Because of his emphasis on the choice of subject matter, his art then had little to do with Picasso's descripton of Cubism as "Art dealing primarily with forms."

Collection:
A private collection

18. ROGER DE LA FRESNAYE
Mans 1885 - 1925 Grasse

Composition au Tambour et à la Trompette, about 1917-1919
Composition with Drum and Trumpet

Watercolor, brush and india ink
260 x 200 mm.; 10 ¼ x 7 1/8 inches

Exhibited:
Cubism & La Section d'Or, The Phillips Collection, Washington, D.C., March- April, Dallas Museum of Art, July, The Minneapolis Institute of Arts, October -November, 1991: no.20 and reproduced in color on p. 69.

Notes:
1. This work was intended to be an illustration for *Tambour*, an unpublished book by Jean Cocteau.
2. Raymond Radiguet (*Les Oeuvres complètes de Raymond Radiguet*, 1952: page 462) explained the significance of the artistic collaboration between Cocteau and La Fresnaye:

> ...Cocteau wrote without thinking in terms of Modernism. There was enough new-ness in Cocteau so that he could still allow himself to enjoy breathing the scent of a flower. One could say the same thing for the artist Roger de La Fresnaye. The images which will appear in *Tambour* are masterpieces of clearness, grace and artistic balance...

Collection:
A private collection

19. MAURICE DE VLAMINCK
Paris 1876 - 1958 Paris

Le vieux Moulin, 1920
The Old Mill

Lithograph
477 x 640 mm.; 18 3/4 x 25 1/4 inches
Signed and numbered

Reference:
Walterskirchen no.156

Notes:
1. An edition of fifty impressions, published in 1921 by Maurice Le Garrec, Paris. This grandiose and monumental work is one of Vlaminck's most important lithographs of the 1920s.
2. The 1920s represented a major period in the history of lithography and in France was particularly distinguished by the works of three artists: Dufy, Matisse and Vlaminck. These same three artists, together with André Derain, also were the significant masters of the *Fauve* woodcut in the years 1904-1907.

20. ALBERT GLEIZES
Paris 1881 -1953 Avignon

Composition, 1920

Mixed media on canvas
890 x 720 mm.; 35 x 28 ¾ inches
Signed Alb Gleizes and dated "20" lower right

Provenance:
Galerie Monique de Groote, Paris
Count Beadouin de Grunne de Hemricourt

Literature:
Michel Massenet *Albert Gleizes*, Paris 1998: illustrated in color on page 53 and on cover

Reference:
Anne Varichon *Albert Gleizes, Catalogue Raisonné*, Paris, 1998, vol. I, no. 936 and illustrated in color on page 322.

Notes:
1. In 1911-1912, appeared a new translation into French of Leonardo da Vinci's *Trattatto della Pittura*. In this treatise, there is a general explanation of the nature and importance of *La Section d'or* (The Golden Section), a triangle whose height is exactly one-half of its length. This so-called "perfect form", to be used in its logical variants (Golden Section triangles, quadrangles and pyramids), served as the basis for the paintings, drawings and prints of particularly Albert Gleizes, Jean Metzinger and Jacques Villon in 1912-1914 and the following decades. The works by these artists, created from 1912 on, represented a new direction in the contemporary art of the time and provided an "answer" to the Cubism of Braque and Picasso. Viewed from the point of view of the Golden Section artists, the works of Braque and Picasso were seen in a negative light as a continuation of Impressionism which both the Cubists and the Golden Section artists had agreed to relegate to a "traditional" past to be rejected by the "new" contemporary art.
2. This very major painting successfully assimilates many of Gleizes' *Section d'or* preoccupations of 1913-1914 and the immediately following years and points forward to Gleizes' directions in the decades following 1918-1920.

21. ALBERT GLEIZES
Paris 1881 -1953 Avignon

L'assiette bleue, 1923
The Blue Dish

Watercolor, wash and pencil on paper
335 x 273 mm.; 13 1/8 x 10 3/4 inches
Signed and dated "AlbGleizes 23"

Provenance:
Huguette Bérès, Paris

Literature:
L'Oeil, September, 1995: no. 474 and illustrated on page 56

Reference:
A. Varichon *Albert Gleizes, catalogue raisonné*, vol. II, Paris, 1998: no. 1132, illustrated on page 372.

Notes:
A fine and sensitively executed example of Gleizes' development in the 1920s, a period in which the *Section d'or* (Golden Section) ideals of 1912-1914 are incorporated into Gleizes' "new painting" of the 1920s and early 1930s.

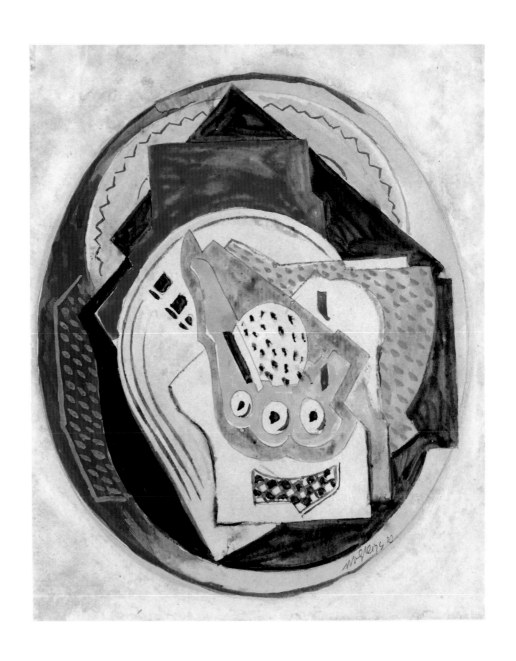

22. ANDRE LHOTE
Bordeaux 1885 – 1962 Paris

Paysage de Lot, circa 1921

Oil on paper, laid down on canvas
540 x 651 mm.; 21 ¼ x 25 5/8 inches
Signed "A. Lhote" lower left

Notes:
In the 1920s, Lhote created some of his most powerful works of which this is an outstanding example. This strong work could be compared to another work executed by Lhote in 1921, *Paysage francais*, number 114 and illustrated in the recent exhibition catalogue: *André Lhote*, Musée de Valence, 2003.

Collection: Private collection, Illinois

23. ANDRE LHOTE
Bordeaux 1885-1962 Paris

Sainte Trinide, 1956

Oil on canvas
500 x 610 mm.; 19 5/8 x 24 inches
Signed lower left and counter-signed and dated "56" on verso

Exhibited:
Andre Lhote, Rétrospective 1907-1962, Artcurial, Paris, 1981: p. 35

Reference:
This painting will be included in the *André Lhote : Complete Works* catalogue presently being prepared by Dominique Bermann-Martin and Jean François Aittouarés.

Notes:
1. Sainte Trinide is a fishing and sea-side town near Sanary, located between Toulon and Marseille. It was one of Lhote's favorite sites on the Mediterranean. A comparable, colorful view of Sainte Trinide by Lhote, also from 1956, was exhibited in: *André Lhote*, Musée de Valence, 2003: no.149.
2. In this and other works of this period, Lhote abandons his structurally based, Golden Section-inspired painting to a lyricism of color, a form of lyricism he had rejected earlier in his career. Fossier (François Fossier, "*Lhote et le paysage*" in: *André Lhote*, Musée de Valence, 2003: p. 51) has described (original text is in French) this development in Lhote's late works in which the artist is more of a *coloriste* than a *plasticien* (creator of forms):

> In reversing the values and the methods which he had conceived twenty years earlier, Lhote returns to a spontaneity...which constitutes the true value of his late works. These [late] works establish Lhote as a more sensitive landscape artist than more generally understood and, in any case, show him to be a colorist of the first order...

(reproduced on page 118)

24. BELA CZOBEL

Budapest 1883 - 1976 Szentendre (Hungary)

Young Girl in White Blouse, about 1960

Oil on canvas
730 x 600 mm.; 28 x 23 1/4 inches
Signed upper left

Notes:

1. In a letter written by Marcel Gromaire to Czóbel in 1963, Gromaire wrote:

    > ...Yes, I have always defended you and this, not through comradship, but because it is my judgement that you are one of the greatest painters of these times. I am particularly sensitive to the intense interior life which animates your painting and to your grave and subtle drawing...

2. In an article written by Raymond Cogniat in *Le Figaro* of March 19, 1964, Czóbel is described:

    > Czóbel, who arrived in Paris in the first years of the Century and who had been contemporary to the great revolutionary movements in Art, had an artistic personality of sufficient strength to have resisted the influences of these various movements and to have preserved an independence which has made of him a truly solitary artist. One could try to associate Czóbel with the Fauve Movement and later with Expressionism, but this would be most arbitrary: Czóbel's sense of liberty has left him with his own, clear-out individuality. Czóbel thus has submitted to no doctrine any more than did Utrillo or Modigliani or Rouault. There is simply in Czóbel's Art a way of feeling profoundly the essence of things; a way of enveloping forms in an atmosphere of dream; a special luminosity in which the object is idealized, and which embraces his subjects with a silent tenderness.

25. ANDRÉ BEAUDIN
Mennecy 1895-1979 Paris

Le Nid, 1944
The Nest

Oil on canvas
730 x 540 mm.; 28 3/4 x 21 1/4 inches
Signed and dated, upper left: *A. Beaudin 1944*

Provenance:
Galerie Louise Leiris, Paris

Notes:
1. A major painting by André Beaudin, one of the group of artists represnted by Daniel H. Kahnweiler, Picasso's dealer from about 1909 onwards. From 1940 on, because of the war situation, Kahnweiler's Galerie Simon (1920-1940) was re-named Galerie Louise Leiris. Louise Leiris was Kahnweiler's step-daughter (née Louise Godon). Kahnweiler's artists were principally: André Beaudin, Georges Braque, Henri Laurens, André Masson, Fernand Léger and Pablo Picasso.
2. André Beaudin had many friends and admirers in French artistic and intellectual circles. Among these was the husband of Louise Leiris, Michel Leiris, one of France's greatest twentieth century writers. Perhaps closest to Beaudin was the poet Paul Eluard (see: *Paul Eluard et ses amis peintres*, Musée National d'Art Moderne, Paris, 1982-83: "Beaudin", pp. 77-78). Beaudin's friendship with Eluard developed just prior to World War II. In 1945, Beaudin illustrated Eluard's publication of *Doubles d'ombre*. In 1946, Eluard wrote the catalogue introduction for Beaudin's retrospective exhibition at Galerie Louise Leiris. In the same year, Beaudin executed his well known bronze *Portrait de Paul Eluard*. In 1949, Eluard wrote an introduction for Beaudin's exhibit at the Buchholz Gallery in New York. Part of that text reads:

> André Beaudin is a bricklayer, an architect, a painter, a sculptor, a printmaker. Going through all his works, there is a red and white flame with reflections of greens and yellows. These are the lands of springtime and the gift of summer.
>
> Paul Eluard
> From: *La correction d'André Beaudin,*
> Buchholz Gallery, New York, 1949.

26. GIORGIO DE CHIRICO
Volos (Greece) 1888-1978 Rome

Apollo e i Tulipani, 1970
Apollo and the Tulips

Watercolor, charcoal, black crayon and pencil
495 x 395 mm.; 19 1/2 x 15 1/2 inches
Signed and dated lower left: "g. de chirico 1970"

Provenance:
Estate of the artist
Carlo Introvigne, Torino
Private collection, Milano

Reference:
Claudio Brunni Sakraischik, *Catalogo Generale Giorgio de Chirico*, Venice 1974: vol. IV, no. 634, illustrated.

Notes:
1. De Chirico was born in Greece of Italian parents. He studied painting in Athens and then, from 1906 to 1909, in Munich at the *Akademie der Bildenen Künste*. In Munich, de Chirico became familiar with the symbolist works of Arnold Böcklin and Max Klinger. He also was quite taken up with the philosophy of Friedrich Nietsche. In 1917, de Chirico met the Italian painter Carlo Carrà with whom he developed the idea of a *pittura metafisica* which went on to become Surrealism. As the principle founder of Surrealism, de Chirico now is recognized as one of the central figures in twentieth century art.

2. De Chirico, always fascinated with the dreams and legends of antiquity, was particularly attracted to the mythological figure of Apollo. Apollo was the son of the gods Zeus and Leto. His twin sister was Artemis, goddess of the hunt. Apollo, the sun god was also the god of light and of truth and of healing. Playing a golden lyre, he was the god of music. Apollo was an archer, shooting with a silver bow, driving his chariot with four horses in order to drive the sun across the sky. People traveled from all over the Greek world in order to visit Apollo's oracle at Delphi. One of the mythological stories relating Apollo to flowers concerns Apollo's atttraction to Hyacinth, a handsome athlete and the son of the king of Sparta. One day, when Apollo and Hyacinth were tossing a discus back and forth, Zephyrs, the god of winds, saw them and became very jealous. He sent a very strong wind in their direction and blew the discus off course. The discus struck the mortal Hyacinth on the temple, resulting in his death. Apollo was so grieved that, as Hyacinth lay dying in his arms, he turned the youth into a flower to give him a measure of immortality. Fragrant flowers are said to have thereupon sprung from the bleeding head of Hyacinth. This same image has been a favorite subject of Surrealism. In this mysterious work by de Chirico, however, instead of the expected hyacinths, there are tulips, flowers which, over the centuries, traditionally have been the symbol of wealth and power.

3. De Chirico, from his artistic beginnings on, was quite taken with the person of Apollo. Many of his "portraits" of the imaginary Apollo were really self-portraits. For examples, there are de Chirico's *The Song of Love* from 1914 (Collection Nelson A. Rockefeller) and his *Philosopher's Promenande* of 1914 (Collection Vicomte Charles de Noailles) which are both close to de

(text continues on page 56)

Chirico's *Self-Portrait* of 1919. Even more remarkable, in this case, is the relation of this pastel to photographs of de Chirico himself (see: Herbert List's photograph of 1949, used as the frontispiece to Jame Thrall Soby's book on de Chirico of 1955).

4. The recognition of de Chirico has been relatively slow in developing in the United States. In 1955, finally appreared the book *Giorgio de Chirico* by James Thrall Soby, published by the Museum of Modern Art in New York. As early as 1957, de Chirico exhibited twenty-four paintings in Chicago at R. S. Johnson Fine Art whose owner at the time, the late S. E. Johnson (1904-1967), had acquired the twenty-four works directly from de Chirico in the latter's studio-apartment on the Piazza Espagna in Rome.

27. ANDRÉ MASSON
Balagny-sur-Thérain 1896-1987 Paris

Une fête, 1958
A Celebration

Pastel
641 x 482 mm.; 25 1/4 x 19 inches
Signed "André Masson" lower left, and titled and dated "1958" on verso

Provenance:
Dr. & Mrs. Philip Falk, Chicago

Exhibited:
In the Mind's Eye: Dada and Surrealism, Museum of Contemporary Art, Chicago, 1985: illustrated in catalogue, p. 186.

Notes:
1. The authenticity of this outstanding, dynamic work has been confirmed by the *Comité Masson*.
2. A close friend of André Breton, Joan Miro and Max Ernst in the early 1920s, Masson was a major figure within the Surrealist movement. Already by the 1930s, however, Masson abandoned that movement and, instead, his art focused on the human condition, a focus that largely had its roots in his reactions (in the same sense as those of Picasso) to the horrors of the Spanish Civil War. In these years, for "dissident Surrealists" such as Antonin Artaud, Georges Bataille, Michel Leiris and Georges Limbour, all of whom are called Surrealism's "enemies from within", Masson's work, on the other hand, possessed a "Dionysian character" which was to challenge Surrealism on its own grounds.
Under the German occupation of France in World War II, Masson's work was condemned as "degenerate". As a result, he fled to Martinique and then to the United States. Masson's often-described arrival in the United States was a rude one in which U.S. Customs officials, finding a group of erotic drawings in his luggage, denounced them as pornographic and tore them up on the spot. In the United States, Masson lived in Preston, Connecticut, and, with Léger and others, became a major influence on American abstract expressionists. After the war, Masson settled in France in Aix-en-Provence where he executed the present work. Over the post-war years, Masson was part of the group of Daniel Kahnweiler's artists (exhibiting at the Galerie

(text continues on page 58)

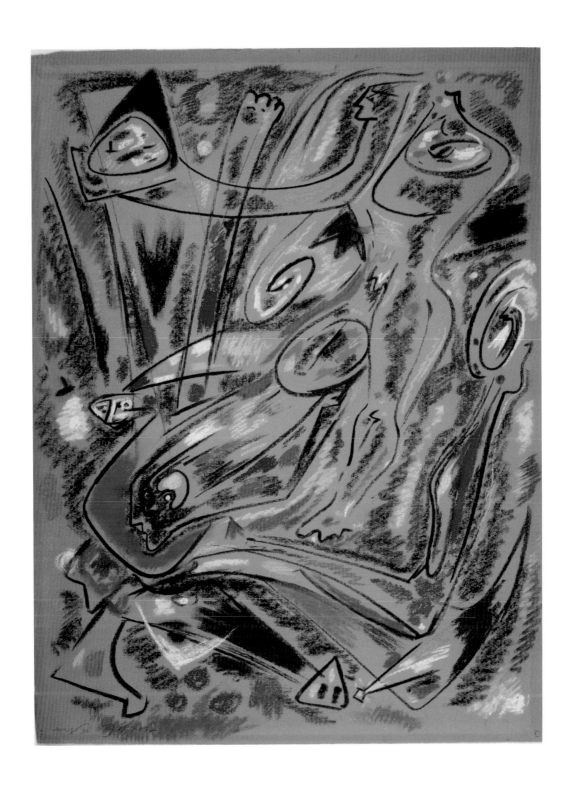

Louise Leiris in Paris). These were principally Beaudin, Braque, Laurens, Léger, Masson and Picasso. In a text from the catalogue *André Masson*, Galerie Louise Leiris in 1972, the artist summed up the nature of his post-surrealist art:

> Today painting has no predestined destination. The artist, conscious or not conscious of this "shipwreck" of art, has only to describe his feelings. This can consist in real or imagined facts: it does not make any difference.
> (*Aujourd'hui ou le tableau n'a aucune destination prévue, le peintre conscient ou non de cette déréliction, n'a d'autre chose à faire que son Journal. Faits "réals", ou faits imaginaires, il n'importe*).

28. JEAN DUBUFFET
Le Havre 1901-1985 Paris

Sourire, 1961
Smile

Lithograph in colors: edition of 50
518 x 378 mm.; 20 3/8 x 14 7/8 inches
Signed "Dubuffet" dated "62" and numbered

Reference:
Webel 812

Notes:
Dubuffet was born in Le Havre and, at the age of seventeen, he moved to Paris to study at the *Académie Julian*. His art studies lasted only six months before he went off on his own and created a very personal style of painting. That form of painting has been characterized with terms such as "madness", "moodiness", "passion" and as the art of the "tormented" and the "insane". More usually Dubuffet's art has been classified as *art brut* ("raw art"). At the same time, there runs through the works of Dubuffet a sentiment of humor, as seen in this work, which in its particular nature is refreshing, quite unique and very different from such sentiments to be found in the works of most of Dubuffet's contemporaries.

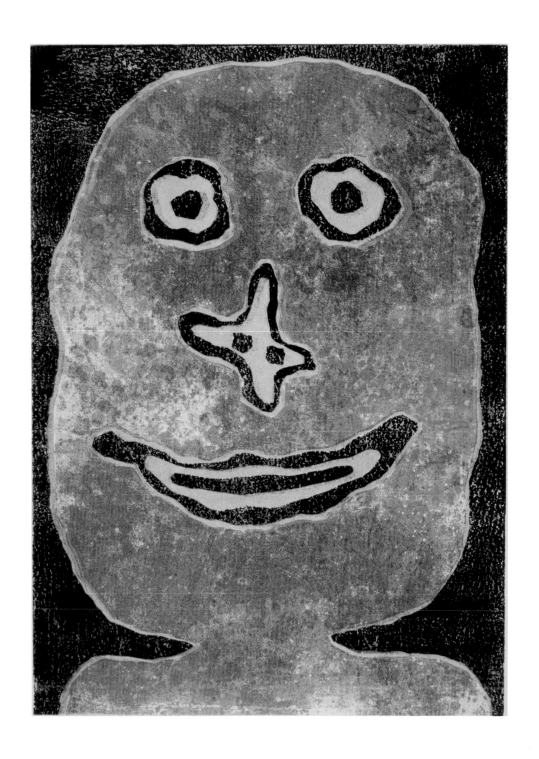

29. MICHAEL AYRTON
London 1921-1975 London

Journey through the Head, 1971

Mixed media
762 x 589 mm.; 30 x 22 inches
Signed and dated lower right

Notes:
1. This is one of Michael Ayrton's most important studies and it relates to the theme of many of his sculptures.
2. Michael Ayrton was born in London in 1921. He was the son of Gerald Gould, the poet, essayist, and literary critic, and Barbara Ayrton, the socialist politician who became Chairman of the Labour Party. Ayrton left school at the age of fourteen to study art. At that early age, Ayrton met Henry Moore and Pavel Tchelitchev. Prolonged stays in Vienna followed and then Paris where he shared a studio with John Minton. In collaboration with Minton, Ayrton did designs for a production of *Macbeth* for John Gielgud. During World War II, Ayrton was conscripted into the Royal Air Force from which he was invalided the following year.

   In 1943, Ayrton had his first exhibit in London. In the following thirty years, works of Michael Ayrton were acquired by over 60 public institutions, mostly in Great Britain and the United States. In those same years, Ayrton wrote twenty-two books, all fascinating, from *British Drawing* in 1946 to *The Midas Consequence* in 1975. In those same years, Ayrton illustrated over 30 books, produced four films and designed three theatrical productions.The bibliography on Michael Ayrton contains over thirty-five authors, including writings by Leonard Baskin, Sir John Gielgud, Robert Hughes, R. Stanley Johnson, Edward Lucie-Smith, David Piper, C. P. Snow, and Rex Warner. In addition, there now is Jacob E. Nyenhuis's recent major 345 page study, published in 2003: *Myth and the Creative Process: Michael Ayrton and the Myth of Daedalus, the Maze Maker*.
3. See Michael Ayrton's remarks on page 62 of this publication.

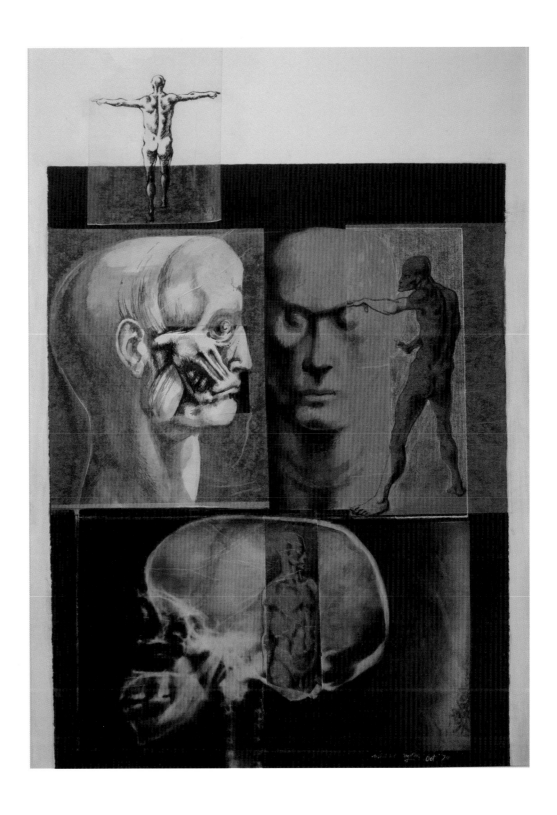

30. MICHAEL AYRTON
London 1921-1975 London

*L'Oiseau chant avec ses Doigts,*1972
The Bird Sings with his Fingers

Mixed media
762 x 533 mm.; 30 x 21 inches
Signed and dated lower right

Notes:
1. This is one of Michael Ayrton's most important studies and it relates to the theme of many of his mytho-psychological sculptures.
2. In 1957, Ayrton wrote (Michael Ayrton, *The Act of Drawing*, Methuen & Co., London, 1957):

> The artist in Western society is encouraged to distrust his intellect. There is a deep-seated urge to see in him something of the "natural", the semi-sacred idiot often revered in primitive societies. What precisely it is in man's memory which fosters this delusion I do not know, but perhaps the menace of the image-maker's magic can thus be partially dispersed or hidden and the disquieting relationship he has with society becomes easier to condone. At all events there is a belief, almost a hope, that the development of sensitivity and the refinement of intuitive emotional responses is incompatible with a keen intelligence. And the artist himself responds to this proposition gladly if he is stupid and silently if he is not. But like many long-sustained conspiracies, the plot eventually deludes the participants. The artist betrays his mind and the public betrays its distaste by requiring less and less from the artist.

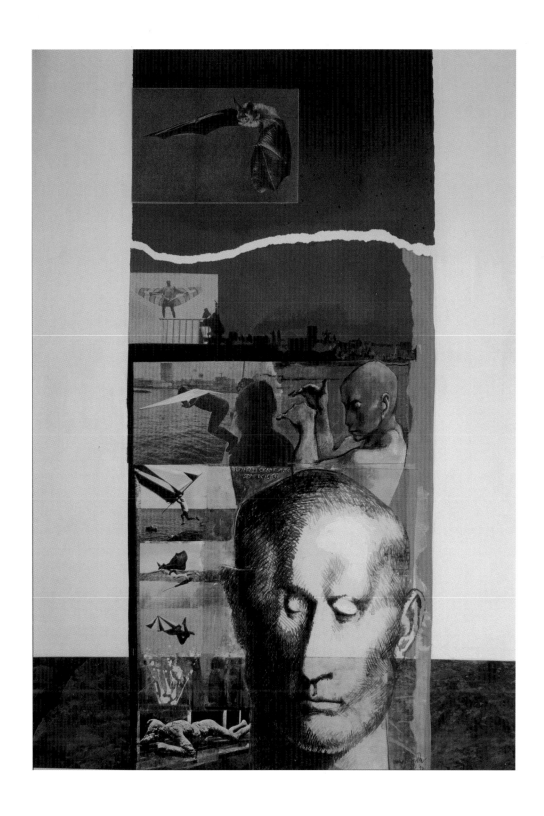

31. DUILIO BARNABÈ

Bologna 1914-1961 French Alps

Vaso Blu, about 1957
Blue Vase

Oil on canvas
810 x 540 mm.; 31 7/8 x 21 1/4 inches
Signed

Provenance:
Private Collection, Switzerland

Notes:
1. A very fine, beautiful and sensitively executed work by Duilio Barnabè.
2. In an article in *Prisme des Arts* (no. 19, Paris, 1959), Jean Bouret wrote:

> I consider Barnabè as the great precursor of future times,
> as the artist who will astonish and mark his epoch with the
> clearest, noblest and most accessible language in the world:
> clearest, noblest and most accessible language because of
> being the most pure.

32. DUILIO BARNABÈ

Bologna 1914-1961 French Alps

Cattedrale, about 1952
Cathedral

Oil on canvas
91 x 143 cm.; 36 x 55 1/2 inches
Titled on verso

Provenance:
The estate of the artist

Notes:
1. An important, early painting by Barnabè, dating from six years or so after his arrival in Paris in 1946.
2. In an article written in *Le Monde* by Michel Concil-Lacoste, the writer described Barnabè:

> Barnabè is a painter of conciliation and of silence, a painter of the
> impossible dialogue. He poses the problem of communication in the
> barest and nudist plastic terms, confounding willingly the animate and
> the inanimate.

33. DUILIO BARNABÈ
Bologna 1914-1961 French Alps

***Corista in rosso e bianco*, 1959-1960**
Choir-Boy in Red and White

Oil on canvas
130 x 97 cm.; 51 ¼ x 38 ¼ inches
Signed lower left

Provenance:
Private Collection, Dallas

Notes:
1. A major painting by Barnabè, dating from about 1959-1960.
2. In his book *Duilio Barnabè* of 2003, p. 15, R. Stanley Johnson writes:

> Whatever the underlying subjects of his paintings, Barnabè
> consistently employed similar artistic methods. First, he
> eliminated what he felt to be nonessential, superficial details and
> then crystallized what he considered to be the irreducible elements
> of any given subject. In his search for purity of expression,
> Barnabè attempted to drive all individual characteristics out of his
> paintings in order to create abstract, universal emblems.
> Barnabè's figures, like those of his Parisian contemporary,
> Alberto Giacometti, are isolated, situated outside of time and
> devoid of fellow human presence. As in Sartre's concept of
> "nothingness" or Dubuffet's *Non-lieux* (No-Place) paintings, the
> monochromatic, cool backgrounds of Barnabè's compositions
> give no clue about time and place and allow no distinction
> between past and present.

69

Works by
Marcel Gromaire

37. Gromaire *Ferryman*, etching, 1928

34. MARCEL GROMAIRE
Noyelles-sur-Sambre 1892 – 1971 Paris

Le jour et la Nuit, circa 1938-1941
Day and Night

Watercolor and ink
385 x 450 mm.; 15 1/8 x 17 3/4 inches
Signed lower right

Provenance:
Vente Briest, Paris, June 20, 1995
Private collection, Paris

Reference:
Certificate of Mme. Françoise Chibret Plaussu and M. François Gromaire, editiors of the *Gromaire: Catalogue Raisonné.*

Notes:
1. This work from about 1938-1941 is one of a series of brilliantly created Gromaire watercolors, all of a similar square format, meant as studies for eventual tapestries.
2. Between 1938-1944, Marcel Gromaire and Jean Lurçat re-invented the European art of tapestry. Gromaire's first tapestry, *La Terre* (Earth) was executed in 1938. Later in 1938, Guillaume Jeanneau, the French publisher and writer (*L'Art Cubiste*, Paris, 1929), asked Gromaire and Lurçat to execute a series of tapestries for France's tapestry center of *Les Gobelins*. These commissions, in the form of watercolors such as this one, were interrupted by the beginning of World War II. This resulted in many of the projected tapestries not being executed. Later, in 1939, Jeanneau renewed his commission, but this time the tapestries were to be executed in France's traditional tapestry-making cities of Aubusson and Felletin. Most of Gromaire's "tapestry watercolors", including this one, were never finalized as actual tapestries. The series of watercolors as a whole, however, remains as one of Gromaire's most masterful achievements.
3. In a letter of Sept. 19, 1941 Gromaire wrote to the art critic Florent Fels, (quoted in: *Marcel Gromaire*, Musée d'Art Moderne de la Ville de Paris, 1980, p. 21):

> …Tapestry should not be considered as simply fabric to be hand-made, but rather as a great mural-art – as in the Middle Ages. In this sense, we again find the great classical tradition of the 14th and 15th centuries…The true significance of the purely technical aspect [of the creation of tapestries] again should be sought after. (The attempts of Dufy at Beauvais, consisting of decorative screens and chairs, were still only copies of paintings). Insofar as I am concerned, over the last two years I have dedicated such a considerable amount of my work to tapestries that I have hardly had any time for painting, and then only to watercolors for my pleasure and research.

35. MARCEL GROMAIRE
Noyelles-sur-Sambre 1892 – 1971 Paris

L'Auto, 1925

Etching
180 x 245 mm.;7 1/8 x 9 5/8 inches
Signed and numbered 9/30

Reference:
L'Oeuvre Gravé de Marcel Gromaire, Vol. I, François Gromaire, 1976: no. 60

Notes:
François Gromaire notes that, although this work is numbered as an edition of thirty, only the first twenty of the edition were printed, signed and numbered over Gromaire's lifetime.

36. MARCEL GROMAIRE
Noyelles-sur-Sambre 1892 – 1971 Paris

La Pêche en barque, 1931
Fishing

Etching
180 x 240 mm.; 7 1/8 x 9 1/12 inches
Signed and numbered 30/30

Reference:
L'Oeuvre Gravé de Marcel Gromaire, Vol. I, François Gromaire, 1976: no. 98

37. MARCEL GROMAIRE
Noyelles-sur-Sambre 1892 – 1971 Paris

Le Passeur, 1928
Ferryman

Etching
240 x 180 mm.; 9 ½ x 7 1/8 inches
Signed and numbered 45/120

Reference:
L'Oeuvre Gravé de Marcel Gromaire, Vol. I, François Gromaire, 1976: no. 60

Notes:
A total edition of 120 impressions plus eight un-numbered artist's proofs. This work was published by the *Société des Amateurs d'art et Collectionneurs*, Paris.

(reproduced on p. 71)

38. MARCEL GROMAIRE
Noyelles-sur-Sambre 1892 - 1971 Paris

Paysan se chauffant, 1939
Peasant Warming Himself

Oil on canvas
100 x 81 cm.; 39 3/8 x 31 7/8 inches
Signed and dated lower right

Verso:
Inscribed: *Gromaire/Paysan se Chauffant/1939*

Exhibited:
Salon d'Automne, Palais des Beaux-Arts, Paris, 1943, no. 549

Literature:
George Besson, *Gromaire*, Braun et Cie, Paris, 1949, no. 30, illustrated
Marcel Zahar, *Gromaire*, Pierre Callier, Geneva, 1961, no 56, illustrated

Reference:
François Gromaire & Françoise Chibret-Plaussu Marcel *Gromaire: Catalogue Raisonné de Peintures*, 1993: no. 501 and reproduced on page 187.

Notes:
A powerful, "expressionist" work, one of Gromaire's outstanding paintings of the 1930s.

Collection:
Private Collection, Arizona

39. MARCEL GROMAIRE
Noyelles-sur-Sambre 1892 – 1971 Paris

Tête de femme, 1937
Head of a Woman

Pen and ink drawing
318 x 243 mm.; 12 ½ x 9 5/8 inches
Signed and dated, lower right

Provenance:
Private US collection

Exhibited:
Seurat to Picasso, R. S. Johnson Fine Art, Chicago, 1998: no. 28 and reproduced on p. 63.

Notes:
In this strong work, we see one of Gromaire's finest drawings from the 1930s.

40. MARCEL GROMAIRE
Noyelles-sur-Sambre 1892 - 1971 Paris

Arbre et Clocher, 1965
Tree and Steeple

Oil on canvas
525 x 636 mm.; 20 ¾ x 25 ¼ inches
Signed and dated "Gromaire 1965" lower right

Verso:
Inscribed: "Gromaire/Arbre et Clocher/1965/JMD"

Provenance:
Galerie David et Garnier, Paris, Carnet no. 703
The Lefevre Gallery, London, 1966
Private European Collector, 2006

Exhibited:
Recent Works by Marcel Gromaire, Lefevre Gallery, London, May 1966

Reference:
François Gromaire & Françoise Chibret-Plaussu *Marcel Gromaire: Catalogue Raisonné de Peintures*, 1993: no. 727 and reproduced on page 256.

Collection:
Private collection, Illinois

Notes:
In *Gromaire*, Musée National d'Art Moderne, Paris, 1963, Jean Cassou wrote:

> ...Every work of Gromaire, whether it be the description of a season or a sunset, or whether it be an urban scene or a human figure, comes back to a "Landscape", a constructed, architectured, organic and luxuriant landscape; something of exteriorness and vastness, which offers an enormous and admirable spectacle for our contemplation... This amplitude of regard and of conception... presents, it seems to me, an accomplishment which is absolutely unique in our time...

41. MARCEL GROMAIRE
Noyelles-sur-Sambre 1892 – 1971 Paris

Le Dessinateur, 1958
The Draughtsman

Etching
198 x 260 mm.; 6 7/8 x 9 3/8 inches
Signed and numbered 10 /75

Reference:
L'Oeuvre Gravé de Marcel Gromaire, Vol.II, François Gromaire, 1976: no. 142

Notes:
Only twenty of the planned edition of 75 were printed, numbered and signed by Marcel Gromaire before his death in 1971 and thus are very rare.

42. MARCEL GROMAIRE
Noyelles-sur-Sambre 1892 – 1971 Paris

Paysage avec des Vaches, 1939
Landscape with Cows

Etching
177 x 237 mm.; 6 7/8 x 9 3/8 inches
Signed and numbered 33/50

Reference:
L'Oeuvre Gravé de Marcel Gromaire, Vol. I, François Gromaire, 1976: no. 117

43. MARCEL GROMAIRE
Noyelles-sur-Sambre 1892 – 1971 Paris

Nu à la Tour Eiffel, 1952
Nude with the Eiffel Tower

Etching
257 x 199 mm.; 10 1/8 x 7 3/4 inches
Signed and numbered 42/50

Reference:
L'Oeuvre Gravé de Marcel Gromaire, Vol. II, François Gromaire, 1976: no. 138

(not reproduced)

44. MARCEL GROMAIRE

Noyelles-sur-Sambre 1892 – 1971 Paris

Nu assis: les bras sur la tête, 1960
Nude Sitting: Her Arms above Her Head

Pen and ink drawing
326 x 248 mm.; 12 ¾ x 9 ¾ inches
Signed and dated "1960", towards lower left

Provenance:
The artist

Exhibited:
Homage to Marcel Gromaire, R. S. Johnson Fine Art, Chicago, 1977: no. 120 of catalogue.
Marcel Gromaire: Works on Paper, R. S.Johnson Fine Art, Chicago, 1987-1988: no. 45 of catalogue.

Notes:
Marcel Gromaire in *Marcel Gromaire : dessinateur*, le musée de poche, Paris, 1973, page 18, has expressed some of his ideas of the process of drawing:

> Abstract? Real? The arbitrary line, that necessary and invented line which
> I draw...That line [whose purpose it is] to limit two forces, to join two
> volumes. Is not this pure abstraction?...And could one believe that an
> image would be complete if it does not attack the skeleton, the living skin
> of human beings, nourished with light? Abstraction, human
> architecture - concrete sensation, pulled from the ground below -
> duality melted into one single, expressive unity.

45. MARCEL GROMAIRE
Noyelles-sur-Sambre 1892 – 1971 Paris

Nu, 1957
Nude

Pen and ink drawing
320 x 250 mm.; 12 5/8 x 9 ¾ inches
Signed and dated, lower right

Provenance: The artist

Exhibited:
Homage to Marcel Gromaire, R. S. Johnson Fine Art, Chicago, 1977: no. 117 of catalogue.
Marcel Gromaire – Works on Paper, R. S. Johnson Fine Art, Chicago, 1987-1988: no. 40 of catalogue.

46. MARCEL GROMAIRE

Noyelles-sur-Sambre 1892 – 1971 Paris

Nu assis, penché à droite, 1960
Nude Sitting, Leaning to the Right

Pen and ink drawing
248 x 325 mm.; 9 ¾ x 12 ¾ inches
Signed and dated, lower right

Provenance:
The artist

Exhibited:
Marcel Gromaire: Works on Paper, R. S. Johnson Fine Art, Chicago, 1987-1988: no. 43 and reproduced on page 73.

Works by
Pablo Picasso

49. Picasso   engraving, 1914

47. PABLO PICASSO
Malaga 1881-1973 Mougins

Modèle et Grande Sculpture de dos, May 4, 1933
Model and Large Sculpture Seen from Behind

Etching on Montval laid paper with *Picasso* watermark: edition of 300
445 x 337 mm.; 17 1/2 x 13 1/4 inches
Signed in pencil by the artist

Reference:
Suite Vollard 73
Bloch 186
Baer 345-IV-Bd

48. PABLO PICASSO
Malaga 1881-1973 Mougins

Minotaure aveugle guidé par une Fillette, I, September 22, 1934
Blind Minotaur Led by a Young Girl, I

Etching on Montval laid paper with *Picasso* watermark: edition of 300
252 x 348 mm.; 10 x 13 3/4 inches
Signed in pencil by the artist

Reference:
Suite Vollard 94
Bloch 222
Baer 434-XII-Bd

49. PABLO PICASSO
Malaga 1881–1973 Mougins

Cliché Kahnweiler, 1914

Engraving on halftone printing plate
110 x 100 mm.; 4 5/16 x 3 15/16 inches
Annotated on verso "tiré par Fort" and bearing, also on verso, the purple, oval stamp of the Succ(ession) Pablo Picasso Coll(ection) Marina Picasso.

Provenance:
Pablo Picasso (estate)
Marina Picasso
Sanford Weiss

Reference:
Geiser 40-VII/VII
Baer 40-VII

(text continues on page 94)

Exhibited:
Cubist Prints/Cubist Books, Donna Stein, Franklin Furnance, New York, 1993, no. 23, illustrated on page 39 and on cover.

Notes:
In this work, Picasso re-worked a negative of another of his cubist period works in the collection of Daniel H. Kahnweiler (1884-1979) who had been Picasso's dealer since about 1907. This is one of only four impressions of this final state. According to Baer, two of these (both printed by the artist) are in the Musée Picasso in Paris (MP 1950 and MP 1951). One of the remaining two impressions (printed by Fort in 1930) is also in the Musée Picasso (MP 1952), while this apparently is the only impression in the final state not in a museum.

(reproduced on page 91)

50. PABLO PICASSO
Malaga 1881–1973 Mougins

La Dormeuse, 1947
Young Woman Sleeping

Lithograph: edition of 50
500 x 650 mm.; 19 3/4 x 25 5/8 inches
Signed and numbered

Reference:
Bloch 435
Mourlot 81

Notes:
The medium of lithography was invented in Munich by Alois Senefelder who published his *Lehrbuch der Steindruckerei* (Teaching Manuel for Printing on Stone) in 1798. The first major period in the history of lithography saw that medium spreading in Germany with artists such as Olivier, Quaglio, Schadow and Schinkel, in England with artists including Blake, Fuseli, Ward and Bonnington, in Italy with Hayez, Longhi, Migliara and others and finally in France with Delacroix, Gericault and Goya (then living in Bordeaux). A second major period in lithography centered in France in the 1830s through the 1860s and was marked particularly by the works of Daumier, but also by those of Bresdin and Gavarni. A third lithographic development came about in the last thirty years of the nineteenth century, starting with Manet, but then going on to Redon, Toulouse-Lautrec, Degas, Pissarro, Gauguin, Bonnard and Vuillard At the same time, this third period included a number of artists as diverse as Corinth, Kirchner, Klimt, Kollwitz, Menzel, Munch and Whistler. A fourth development in the use of lithography came to a head in the 1920s and the names of Dufy, Matisse and Vlaminck would all have to be mentioned. The fifth and last major period in the history of lithography is concentrated in the years of 1945-1960 and is dominated by one artist: Picasso

51. PABLO PICASSO
Malaga 1881-1973 Mougins

Vénus et l'Amour, d'après Cranach, 1949
Venus and Cupid, after Cranach

Aquatint on Rives paper: edition of 50
783 x 427 mm.; 30 ¾ x 16 3/8 inches
With artist's signature stamp and numbered

Reference:
Bloch 1835
Baer 876-VI-Ba

Notes:
1. This is one of Picasso's great graphic achievements. The work was executed by the artist in 1949, and finally printed in 1961, but was not published by his dealer until after the death of the artist.
2. This aquatint, after a painting by one of Picasso's favorite old master artists: Lucas Cranach (1472-1553), is one of two major graphic works by Picasso after Cranach, the other being *David and Bethsheba*, also of 1949.
3. The story behind this work is that Picasso's dealer, Daniel Kahnweiler, sent from Germany to Picasso, a postcard reproducing Cranach's masterpiece, *Venus and Cupid*. Using only the reproduction of this work by Cranach as his inspiration, Picasso created this magnificent aquatint.

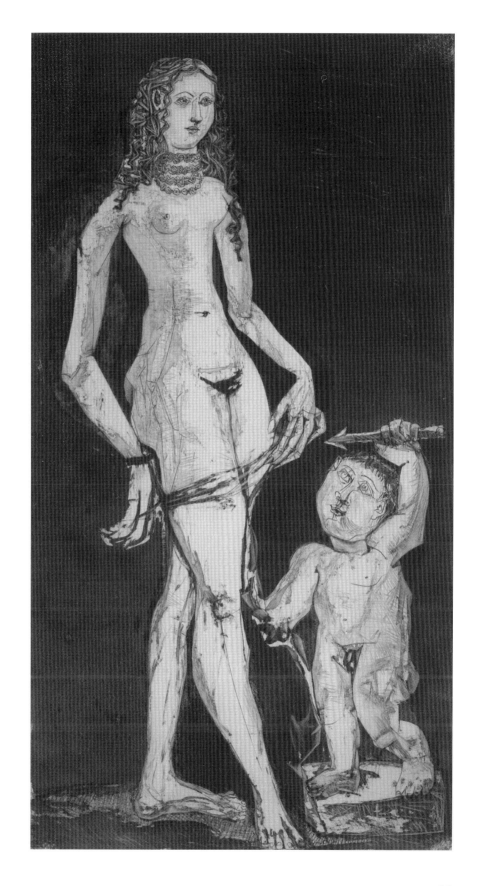

52. PABLO PICASSO
Malaga 1881–1973 Mougins

Hommage à Bacchus, 1960
Homage to Bacchus

Lithograph on *Arches* paper: edition of 50
495 x 637 mm.; 19 ½ x 25 inches
Signed and numbered 48/50

Provenance:
Jean and Suzanne Planque

Reference:
Bloch 1006
Mourlot 336

Notes:
1. This lithograph was executed in a particularly happy and fulfilled period in Picasso's life, at a time when he was 79 years old. Picasso seems to associate himself personally here with the figure of Bacchus. This magnificent composition, overflowing with the joy of life, reflects the artist's sentiments as he became older.
2. The former owner of this work, Jean Planque (1910-1998), had worked from 1954 to 1972 for the Basel dealer Ernst Beyeler. Later he moved with his wife Suzanne to a small town in southern France where he wrote his memoires and also published numerous texts on various contemporary artists, particularly Dubuffet. Planque and his wife Suzanne (died 1995) brought together a major collection, including particularly works by Braque, Cézanne, Dubuffet, Gris, Klee, Léger and Picasso. After the death of Planque in 1998, his remaining collection was shown for the first time in 2001 at the Musée de l'Hermitage in Lausanne.

53. PABLO PICASSO
Malaga 1881-1973 Mougins

La Mère et les Enfants, January 20, 1953
Mother and her Children

Lithograph: edition of 50
480 x 740 mm.; 18 7/8 x 29 1/8 inches
Signed and numbered

Reference:
Bloch 739
Mourlot 239

Notes:
1. In 1945-1949, Picasso took refuge in the printing shop of Fernand Mourlot in Paris. In these years, he began his great series of lithographs, created over some fifteen years until around 1960.
2. In the late 1940s, Picasso met the artist Françoise Gillot with whom he had two children: Claude and Paloma. There followed a series of drawn, lithographed and etched portraits of Françoise Gillot and of their two children. The present work is one of the most remarkable of this series.
3. Françoise Gillot appears to have been the only woman in Picasso's life who was known to have left the artist. She later married the developer of the Salk vaccine, Dr. Jonas Salk.

54. PABLO PICASSO
Malaga 1881-1973 Mougins

Pique (Noir et Beige) 1959
Bullfight (in Black and Beige)

Linocut in colors: edition of 50
620 x 750 mm.; 24 3/8 x 29 ½ inches
Signed and numbered

Literature:
Picasso: Linoleum Cuts, The Metropolitan Museum of Art, New York, 1985: no. 14 and illustrated in color on page 30.
Picasso Linoleum Cuts: Bacchanals, Women, Bulls & Bullfighters, Harry N. Abrams, New York, 1963 (1988 edition) no. 6 (illustrated in color).

Reference:
Bloch 909
Baer 1226/II/B/b

Notes:
Picasso created his first major multi-colored linocut in Vallauris in 1958. That work, *Bust of Woman after Cranach*, was made in six colors, each necessitating a separate piece of linoleum. The resulting linocut was an aesthetic failure in that the colors harmonized poorly. It was a technical failure as well in that the forms and colors did not correlate satisfactorily as a result of the individual plates not registering correctly. Part of Picasso's problem with that work was that he had to cut and print each lino-block separately. This lengthy procedure resulted in a discontinuity of the creative process and took away much of the spontaneity, so essential in Picasso's most successful works. Through sheer artistic necessity, therefore, Picasso was driven to invent a new technique for producing multi-colored linocuts. Instead of using one block for each color, as had been the case in all the various forms of relief printing since the Renaissance, Picasso devised a reductive technique to produce all the colors from only one piece of linoleum on which a preliminary, detailed guide-drawing first had been executed by the artist. One problem with this method is that after each color (or "state") has been printed and the lino-block has been cut away to prepare for the printing of the next color, it becomes impossible to amend or revise the previous state. In the Italian Renaissance, indeed in the whole history of relief printing, the techniques utilized had always made it possible for the artist to re-work individual color blocks. In Picasso's method of the multi-colored linocut, however, there was no way to return to a previous state and the work could only be corrected progressively. Picasso's unique artistic abilities allowed him to overcome this technical difficulty, a difficulty that he turned to his advantage as evidenced by his increasingly simplified and powerful multi-colored linocuts.

55. PABLO PICASSO
Malaga 1881-1973 Mougins

Le Modèle, 1965
The Model

Aquatint with etching
380 x 275 mm.; 15 x 10 3/4 inches
Signed and numbered by the artist

Reference:
Bloch 1200
Baer 1182

Notes:
1. From the group of ten aquatints executed by Picasso in 1965 and called *Sable Mouvant.*
2. The painter and model was one of Picasso's preferred subjects over his entire career, but particularly during the last decade of his life. Picasso executed a series of paintings on that subject in 1963. There followed a number of "painter and model" etchings, including this one, in 1965-1966. The seemingly inexhaustible, creative variations on this subject were the central elements in his *347 Series* of etchings of 1968 and then in his *156 Series* of 1969-1972.

56. PABLO PICASSO
Malaga 1881-1973 Mougins

Grand Nu de Femme, 1962
Large Nude Woman

Linocut in colors: edition of 50
635 x 526 mm.; 25 x 20 ¾ inches
Signed and numbered

Literature:
Picasso: Linoleum Cuts, The Metropolitan Museum of Art, New York, 1985: no. 84 and illustrated in color on page 83.

Reference:
Bloch 1085
Baer 1309/VI/B/a (from b)

Notes:
A very fine, richly colored impression with pristine colors of one of the most powerful and accomplished linocuts in the history of that medium.

57. PABLO PICASSO
Malaga 1881-1973 Mougins

Peintre et modèle, October 20, 1966
Painter and Model

Etching and aquatint: edition of 50
275 x 380 mm.; 10 7/8 x 15 inches
Signed and numbered

Reference:
Bloch 1381
Baer 1403-Bb

Notes:
The painter and model was one of Picasso's preferred subjects over his entire career, but particularly during the last decade of his life. Picasso executed a series of paintings on that subject in 1963. There followed a number of "painter and model" etchings, including this one, in 1965-1966. Finally, the subject was the central element in his *347 Series* of etchings of 1968 and then in his *156 Series* of 1969-1972. Since each of these works treats the same subject, but is very different one from another, these various "painters and models" are a perfect demonstration of the creative genius of this artist.

58. PABLO PICASSO
Malaga 1881-1973 Mougins

Avant la Pique, Cannes, September 8,1959
Before the Lance

Linocut in colors: edition of 50
540 x 665 mm.; 21 1/4 x 26 1/8 inches
Signed and numbered by the artist

Literature:
Picasso: Linoleum Cuts, The Metropolitan Museum of Art, New York, 1985: no. 21 and illustrated in color on page 35.
Picasso Linoleum Cuts: Bacchanals, Women, Bulls & Bullfighters, Harry N. Abrams, New York, 1963 (1988 edition) no. 38 and illustrated in color.

References:
Bloch 941
Baer 1224-II-Ba

Notes:
This is a particularly accomplished and elegant linocut of Picasso. It is a perfect example of Picasso's ability to create new forms which in themselves and in their juxtaposition, one with another, have their own aesthetic and artistic beauty.

59. PABLO PICASSO
Malaga 1881–1973 Mougins

Artiste-peintre avec un modèle qui boude, 4 October 1968
Painter-Artist with Sulking Model

Etching: edition of 50
225 x 325 mm.; 9 x 15 ¾ inches

Reference:
Plate 346 of the *347 Series*
Bloch 1826
Baer 1843-Bb1

Notes:
This work is the next to last etching in the *347 Series* and fittingly is a "painter and model". This was Picasso's preferred and most highly developed theme in the last decade of his life. This etching, with its graphic touches of genius which only Picasso could have achieved, and with its aura of humor surrounding the "sulking model" being depicted by an apparently rather shy artist, is one of the Master's very sensitively conceived treatments of the painter and model.

60. PABLO PICASSO
Malaga 1881–1973 Mougins

Le Matin. Deux femmes au Réveil, November 15, 1959
Morning. Two Women Awakening

Linocut in colors: edition of 50
530 x 643 mm.; 20 7/8 x 25 3/8 inches
Signed and numbered

Literature:
Picasso: Linoleum Cuts, The Metropolitan Museum of Art, New York, 1985: no. 10 and illustrated in color on page 26.
Picasso Linoleum Cuts: Bacchanals, Women, Bulls & Bullfighters, Harry N. Abrams, New York, 1963 (1988 edition) no. 21 and illustrated in color.

Reference:
Bloch 924
Baer 1252-II-Ba

61. PABLO PICASSO
Malaga 1881–1973 Mougins

156 Series: No. 13, February 11 and 28, and March 3, 16 and 30, 1970

Etching and scraper: edition of 65
511 x 642 mm.; 20 1/8 x 25 1/4 inches
Signed with signature stamp, annotated: E. A. (*épreuve d'artiste*), numbered IX/XV

Formerly Collection
Marina Picasso, stamp on verso

Reference:
Bloch 1868
Baer 1873-IX/B/b

Notes:
1. Over his lifetime, Picasso created various *suites* of graphic works. The first of these was the group of fourteen etchings called the *Saltimbanques*, executed in 1904-1905 and published by Ambroise Vollard in 1913. A second group, dating from 1930 to 1936, totaled ninety-seven relatively unrelated and separately conceived works. To these Picasso added three portraits of Vollard. The resulting 100 etchings are now known as the *Suite Vollard*. Still later, in a period of seven months extending from March through October, 1968, Picasso gave up most of his painterly activities and produced a series of 347 etchings, now called the *347 Series*. Later, between June 1969 and March 1972, Picasso created 156 more etchings now known as the *156 Series*. The *156 Series* was Picasso's last major group of prints. The editions consisted of 65 impressions each: 50 numbered 1/50 through 50/50 and 15 numbered I/XV through XV/XV. Each impression from this series was signed with Picasso's signature stamp.
2. This work, the thirteenth of the *156 Series*, was the most technically complex of the whole series and in fact is one of the most technically complex graphic works created in the entire history of printmaking to date. It was worked and reworked by Picasso in nine separate states over a period of some fifty days from February 11 to March 30, 1970.

117

23. André Lhote   Sainte Trinide, 1956